Solo Scenes
from
Great Writers

SOLO SCENES
FROM
GREAT WRITERS

ARRANGED FOR PERFORMANCE

BY

SYDNEY THOMPSON

SAMUEL FRENCH

New York - Toronto - Los Angeles

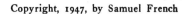

"The Divided Horsecloth" by Bernier is reprinted from
*Aucassin and Nicolette, and Other Medieval Romances and
Legends,* translated by Eugene Mason, Everyman's Li-
brary, by permission of E. P. Dutton & Co.

"The Little Angel" is reprinted from *Little Angel and
Other Stories* by Leonide Andreyev, translated from the
Russian by W. H. Lowe, by permission of Alfred A. Knopf,
Inc. Copyright, 1924, by Alfred A. Knopf, Inc.

FOREWORD

These tales are some that I have given during the past fifteen years in many parts of the world. They have held the attention of audiences and I believe that when they are done with honesty they will continue to do so, for they are the work of the masters of the short story.

The performer who presents them may feel herself part of a long and honorable tradition. For centuries the person who could tell a good story has been welcomed with the seat nearest the fire, the tallest flagon of wine and the choicest cut of venison. In the days when there were no newspapers and few books and theatres the story teller took the place of historian, radio announcer, news analyst, editor, dramatist, actor, critic, popularizer of science, keyhole reporter and commentator on love, religion, family life, kings and their mistresses, crimes and G-men and national glory.

This was especially true of the old ballads, which, even more truly than the works of a Boccaccio or a Maupassant, were the literary expression of a civilization. The names of the authors are lost in the mists of the past, but they have left us a picture of that vanished time—the colorful adventurous life, the gaiety, the pathos, the savagery, the profound religious emotion—all presented with the quick movement, the direct simplicity of statement that is the essence of the ballad. Not even Maupassant could have shown more clearly the pathos of Annie of Lochroyan, when she bids her love open the door. And the decisive, though lachrymose, action of the abducted damsel in "The Outlandish Knight," when she pushes the villain into the sea, amuses us, even while we realize that it is true character drawing.

The ballads come naturally to the performer's lips, not only because of their simplicity, but because we feel instinctively that they are the heritage of our common past. Even the city dweller of today knows them for a link with our forefathers, who used to gather around the hearth fire of a winter evening, to sing or listen to these ancient tales. It is not chance that makes the ballads still alive today. In the mountains of Kentucky and Virginia and by the harbors of Newfoundland and Nova Scotia the descendants of those same Scotch and English people still sing these songs.

The stories of Tristram and of Eliduc are also taken from the realm of folk lore, though in both cases the tale has been formed for us through the artistry of a literary craftsman.

Marie de France, who wrote the beautiful Lay of Eliduc, lived in the latter part of the twelfth century and passed part of her life at the court of the English king, Henry II. She traveled among the Breton people of her own land and collected from them the gems of folk lore and adapted them in her Lays, of which eight or nine survive. She seems to me to be one of the truly great women writers of all time. Certainly in the wife of Eliduc she has set before us a character that is hard to match for nobility and loyalty and self sacrifice.

I have cut the story drastically and its simple sentences can only suggest the emotion that the performer must convey. As an example of this challenge I might cite the sentence, "She bare it to the altar, and though her heart grew dead within her she laid it on the damsel's lips." In these few words must be expressed, first, the joy with which the wife realizes that the magic flower will bring the dead maiden back to life, then the shock of realization of what this will mean to her own happiness, then the resolve and dedication and self sacrifice with which she advances to the altar and stoops and, in tenderness and sorrow, brings her rival back to life.

Tristram and Iseult and Iseult of the White Hands were the central figures in Celtic myths which subsequently appeared in all European literatures. Of the old romances of Tristram, those by Chretien de Troies and La Chevre have disappeared. Parts remain of the versions of Beroul and of Thomas of Ercildonne, twelfth century Norman trouveres, also fragments of poems and the courtly epic, written by Gottfried von Strassburg in 1210. The present version is arranged and cut from the French of Joseph Bedier, based partly on a translation by Florence Simmonds and partly on one by Hilaire Belloc.

When we come to the tales from The Decameron we are entering a world enormously picturesque and romantic and requiring of the performer great economy of presentation if it is not to be submerged in the very richness of its own imagination. In arranging these stories I have cut them practically to the bone, throwing on the performer the responsibility of filling in the sentences with every device of intonation, pause, posture and facial expression.

In Griselda's brief lines the artist must create the entire character of the suffering woman, whose patience has become a household word. The two comedies, "Peronella" and "Chichibio," must be presented with speed, gaiety and above all a kind of forthright robustness, very different from the wordly, subtle sophistication that will be required in Maupassant's humor. In "Madam Catalina" there is suggested an overtone of darkness and horror, leading into the restrained and final sadness with which Messer Gentile gives the lady back to her husband. I would call the performer's attention to what can be done in the way of suggestion and dramatic effect with such simple lines as, "He recalled the strayed life to the lady until she raised her eyes and knew him. And when she would have cried aloud she looked about her and apprehended where she was. And she lay silent." In the second of those three sentences there is an opportunity for everything that you can convey of terror and slowly dawning horror. The last story, "Ghismonda," is the perfect flowering of beauty and sadness, of love and the heroic bearing of a blow and of death. When Ghismonda takes the cup and uncovers it and understands what it holds she is the incarnation of all the lovely tragic heroines who stand in a final moment of frozen incredulity before they leave the world that has no longer anything to give them.

Giovanni Boccaccio was born in 1313 and lived through the most appalling natural calamity that has ever befallen Europe, the terrible, almost incredible

Black Death, of 1348. It has been estimated that one quarter of the population of Europe died. Three out of every five persons died in Florence alone. People said that the end of the world had come—and it was in truth the end of the Middle Ages. Boccaccio has set his Decameron in an exquisite villa garden on the slopes under Fiesole, where a group of youths and maidens have fled to escape the pestilence in Florence. They pass the time in telling stories—stories that are by turns tragic, comic, satiric, romantic—that depict all the glow and pageantry of that bright world that was sinking under the terror of the Black Death.

To this vast and brilliant treasure house of romance countless writers, down to our own day, have turned for inspiration. It marks the first complete departure from the stilted classicism of contemporary literature. Its vivid stories, a hundred tales of all lands and times, are spun on a fine thread of the narrative of the day-by-day doings of the merry gracious company in the villa near Florence. And in the background, like some terrible dark frame for a sunny picture, is the Great Plague.

The performer who wishes to use musical interludes between the stories, played on an unseen piano, will enjoy collecting and arranging the airs that suit her best. I used arrangements from early Italian and French sources: a "Lucis Creator" from an early mass; an old Gagliarda and Pavane, taken from Arbeaud's Orchesographie; a traditional "Dies Irae;" a fifteenth century Villanella and several Troubadour Airs.

Guy de Maupassant was a pupil of Gustave Flaubert, who taught him his profession of observer and writer.

By temperament and education Maupassant was a realist. He had learned from his master that anything is worthy of art when an artist knows how to fashion it. In his stories the boulevards of Paris, the salons, the homes of the bourgeoisie are eternally alive. He is most at home in dealing with ordinary scenes and ordinary people and his characters seldom achieve greatness, either in heroism or wickedness. He prided himself on describing nothing that he had not seen. In that field of realism he is inimitable. Probably no one has been so incredibly deft in the rapid portrayal of a scene or a character. He states his story with a simplicity, a brevity and wit that make it unforgettable.

In presenting these tales the performer must do so with directness and economy of style and at the same time with a hint of French elegance and chic. She might imagine herself to be a lady of the last century, sitting, perhaps, at a café table in the Bois and relating to some interested companions the stories of their contemporary, Monsieur de Maupassant.

The situation in such a tale as "How He Won the Legion of Honor" should be handled with lightness, sophistication and a shrug of amusement. The same situation in "The False Gems" should produce more genuine pity for the deceived husband, as befits the more emotional character of the story. But the final paragraph must be tossed off with a return to the mood of amused comment on the foibles of humanity. "The Fishing Excursion" calls, of course, for all the sincerity and dramatic power of which the performer is capable. "The Minuet" is an expression of remembered loveliness, a tribute to the beauty of that vanished century that has left in the world "the fragrance of love."

I must, I suppose, confess that "The Minuet," as I have called it, is a combination of two of Maupassant's stories, "The Dancers" and "Julie Romain." It is the only case in which I have permitted myself such a liberty. I can only hope that the author would not have considered it too great a one.

For the musical interludes between the stories I turned, naturally, to French folk songs or to music that might have been played in Paris during the time when Maupassant was writing. I used a waltz of the period for the entrance and exit music. After "A Strange Love" I used a few bars from a grave old French dance; after "The Legion of Honor" the folk song "Auprès de ma blonde"; after "Regret" a few bars from "Plaisir d'amour"; preceding "The Fishing Excursion," the military air, "En passant par la Lorraine" and following the same tale a few bars from an old funeral march, blending into the opening measures of "La Marseillaise." To lead into "The Minuet" and also to follow it I would suggest eight or ten bars from the "Dance of the Shades," from Gluck's "Orfeo" or the old "Minuet d'Exaudet."

Count Tolstoi's great story, "Where Love Is God Is," ranks among the world's masterpieces not only for its artistry, but because it is so deeply expressive of the humanity that was the crowning grace of Tolstoi's art. When he wrote it he had left the social and literary world, where his success of every sort had been most brilliant, and had retired to his estates to find among the poor people and the laborers of the countryside the peace that only toil could bring him. He soon found that he must work hard every day, or he would begin to die at heart, and so he believed must every man. The wisdom that he learned from toil and simple living was that life has no meaning and no happiness except as it is spent for others.

On one occasion, after he had visited a night shelter in Moscow and had observed the homeless, destitute and starving men, he wrote, "I know now that the presence of such poverty in our midst, whilst I live comfortably, cover my floors and feed my horses and myself, constitutes a sin which I not only condone but take an active part in."

To Tolstoi religion was not something that applied to a vague and distant future but a living force that determined his relation to the life about him. Otherwise it was not worthy of the name of religion. If the performer can convey to the audience something of this feeling she will have been true to the spirit of the writer.

And that is probably the goal to aim at in all these tales. In themselves they are great art. The performer can do nothing to add to them. She can only hope to make herself a channel—and let the tale come through.

S.T.

CONTENTS

Foreword . . . . **v**

Marie de France

   THE LAY OF ELIDUC **1**

Old Ballads

   THE OUTLANDISH KNIGHT **5**

   THE LASS OF LOCHROYAN **8**

   THE HOLY WELL **13**

   SIR ARTHUR AND CHARMING MOLLEE **16**

   CUPID'S GARDEN **18**

Bernier

   THE DIVIDED HORSECLOTH **20**

      TRANSLATED BY EUGENE MASON

   THE ROMANCE OF TRISTRAM AND ISEULT . . . **24**

      BASED ON THE VERSION BY JOSEPH BEDIER

Giovanni Boccaccio

   GRISELDA **29**

   PERONELLA **31**

   MADAM CATALINA **33**

   CHICHIBIO **35**

   GHISMONDA **37**

      ARRANGED FROM THE TRANSLATION OF JOHN PAYNE

Guy de Maupassant

   A STRANGE LOVE 40

   HOW HE WON THE LEGION OF HONOR 44

   REGRET 48

   A FISHING EXCURSION 52

   THE MINUET 56

   THE FALSE GEMS 60

     ANONYMOUSLY TRANSLATED

Alphonse Daudet

   THE LAST LESSON 66

     ANONYMOUSLY TRANSLATED

Leonide Andreyev

   THE LITTLE ANGEL 70

     ARRANGED FROM THE TRANSLATION OF W. H. LOWE

Leo Tolstoi

   WHERE LOVE IS GOD IS 75

Solo Scenes
from
Great Writers

The Lay of Eliduc

MARIE DE FRANCE

Twelfth Century

There dwelt in Brittany a knight called Eliduc, and he had a wife that was fair and dear to him beyond all measure. It chanced that he journeyed into another country for a space and while he was there he saw the daughter of the king of that country. And each cast great love to other, so that there is no tongue to tell of their loves. And she sent him a scarf and a ring and he was her true friend.

When the summer was come it fell that his liege lord sent word that he should come again to Brittany. But he might not leave his lady, nor would she suffer him to depart from her, so he took her with him and set her on the ship, for to travel with him into Brittany.

As they traveled there arose a great storm and a seaman said to him, "Lo, by thy sin is this storm come, —that thou hast one wife and bringest yet another with thee!"

Now when she heard that her love was wed the damsel swooned and lay dead. Then Eliduc took her in his arms and when they were come to land he bare her to the shore and he laid her in a chapel hard by his own castle. Before the altar he laid her. And he set candles of wax at her head and at her feet. And so he went to his castle, mourning and stricken that near his heart to brast within him. And each day he went to the chapel, to weep beside his love.

Then said his wife, "My lord, my heart is heavy that thou art ever so heavy of heart. Truly would I give all my joy if so be thou mightest find peace."

And when he held his counsel she went from him and required her page to follow where his lord walked in the wood and bring her word again. And on a day, when that Eliduc was far afield with his liege lord, she required the page to lead her whither Eliduc was wont to go.

So went the page and the wife between the trees till they were come to the chapel in the woods. The doors of it were shut, so she set her hand to them and opened them and looked within. And she was ware of candle light, as it had been on an altar. And when she would have entered she saw a little weasel, how he sat upon the threshold.

The wife said, "Slay now this weasel, lest it profane this holy place."

So the page slew the weasel with his staff, and she entered in.

Then she saw, how there lay before the altar a damsel and how she had candles of wax at her head and at her feet.

And the wife said, "See now this woman—like a gem for beauty!" Then the tears brake in her eyes and she kneeled down and said, "She is the love of my lord! And 'tis for her he maketh such lament! And, by my troth, I marvel not thereat, sith so fair a woman hath perished. What for pity and what for love I shall never know joy again."

Now, while she wept, there came the mate of the weasel that was slain and strove to waken it. And when it might not, it went into the forest and it brought a little scarlet flower and laid it on the dead mate's mouth. And the weasel that was dead arose and lived!

Then did the wife give a great cry and she took the herb where it had fallen and she said, "Flower of Life! Oh, Blessed Virgin, who hast sent me this!"

She bare it to the altar and though her heart grew dead within her she laid it on the damsel's lips.

Then the damsel sat up and when remembrance was come she wept that her love was gone from her.

And the wife said, "Ah, little maid, thou art not forsaken and betrayed! Not thou! He thinketh you to be dead and he is so out of all comfort that it is a pity to see. Each day he cometh to look upon you and he deemeth you lifeless, beyond all doubt. I am his wife. And my heart is heavy for you both."

Then the damsel did look upon her and was silent and the wife said,

"Great joy have I that you are on live. I will take you with me and give you back to your friend and for my part I will cry him quit of all and will take the veil."

Then she led the damsel by the hand to where Eliduc sat in his castle and she said, "Little maid, there sits one who shall wipe away all the tears from your eyes." She went into the castle and she said, "Eliduc, great joy awaits thee here. Prithee, kiss me but once—and then never no more!"

But when she saw him, how he made a great cry and sped past her to the damsel, she said no more in words, but she turned her from him to the Holy Mother's house.

AVE, MARIA, GRATIA PLENA ; DOMINUS TECUM ; BENE-DICTA TU IN MULIERIBUS—

The Outlandish Knight

AN OLD ENGLISH BALLAD

"An outlandish knight came from the northlands,
    And he came a-wooing of me.
He said he'd take me away to the northlands
    And there he'd marry me."

"Go get me some of your father's gold
    And some of your mother's fee,
And two of the best nags out of the stable,
    Where there stand thirty and three."

She got him some of her father's gold
    And some of her mother's fee,
And two of the best nags out of the stable,
    Where there stood thirty and three.

He mounted her on the milk white steed,
    Himself on the dapple gray,
And they rode till they came to the salt sea,
    Three hours before the day.

"Light down, light down, my pretty lady,
    And deliver them up to me,
For it's six pretty maidens I have drowned here
    And the seventh you shall be.

"Take off, take off your velvet gown
    And deliver it up to me,

5

For I wot it looks all too rich and too fine,
   To rot in the salt sea.

"Take off, take off your linen smock
   And deliver it up to me,
For it's six pretty maidens I have drowned here,
   And the seventh you shall be."

"If I must take off my linen smock,
   Pray turn your back on me,
For it is not meet that a ruffian like you
   A naked woman should see."

He turned his back upon her then,
   And bitterly did she weep.
She took him about the middle so sma'
   And tumbled him into the deep.

"Lie there, lie there, thou false-hearted man!
   Lie there, instead of me!
For it's six pretty maidens you have drowned here,
   But the seventh hath drownded thee!"

She's mounted her on the milk white steed
   And she led the dapple gray,
And she rode till she came to her father's halls,
   An hour before the day.

The parrot was up in the window so high
   And seeing the lady did say,

"I fear that some ruffian hath led you astray,
    That you tarried so long away!"

"Now prittle no prattle, my pretty parrot,
    And tell no tales on me,
And your cage shall be made of good red gold
    And your perch of ivory."

The king was up in his tower so high
    And hearing the parrot did say,
"What ails thee, what ails thee, my pretty parrot,
    That you prattle so long before day?"

"It's no laughing matter," the parrot did say,
    "That so loudly I call unto thee.
The cats have got into the window so high,
    And I fear they will get me!"

"Well turned, well turned, my pretty parrot,
    Well turned away from me!
Your cage shall be made of the best red gold
    And your perch of ivory!"

The Lass of Lochroyan

A SCOTTISH BALLAD

"Oh, who will build a bonny ship,
　　And set it on the sea?
For I will go to seek my love,
　　My ain love, Gregory."

Her father's built a bonny ship
　　And set it on the sea.
The mast was o' the beaten gold,
　　The sails o' cramoisie.

The sides were o' the gude stout oak,
　　The deck o' mountain pine,
The anchor o' the silver shene,
　　The ropes o' silken twine.

She hadna sailed but twenty leagues,
　　But twenty leagues and three,
When she met wi' a rank robber,
　　And a' his company.

"Now are ye Queen of Heaven hie,
　　Come to pardon a' our sin,
Or are ye Mary Magdalene,
　　Was born in Bethlehem?"

"I'm no the Queen of Heaven hie,
   Come to pardon a' your sin,
Nor am I Mary Magdalene,
   Was born in Bethlehem.

"But I'm the lass of Lochroyan,
   That's sailing on the sea,
To see if I can find my love,
   My ain love, Gregory."

"Oh, see ye na yon stately tower
   Built on the rock of height?
Lord Gregory is within the bower,
   That shines so clear and bright."

She sailed it round and sailed it round
   And loud and loud cried she,
"Now break, now break your fairy charms
   And set my true love free!"

She's ta'en her young son in her arms
   And to the door she's gane,
And long she knocked and sair she cried,
   But answer got she nane.

"Oh, open the door, Lord Gregory!
   Oh open and let me in!
The wind blows loud and cold, Gregory,
   The rain drops fra my chin.

"The shoe is frozen to my foot,
   The glove unto my hand,

The wet drops fra my yellow hair,
　　Na longer can I stand."

Oh, up and spake his ill mother,
　　An ill death may she dee,
"Ye're no the lass of Lochroyan,
　　She's far out owre the sea.

"Awa, awa, ye ill woman,
　　Ye're no come here for gude,
Ye're but some witch or wil' warlock,
　　Or mermaid o' the flood."

"I'm neither witch nor wil' warlock,
　　Nor mermaid o' the sea,
But I'm Annie of Lochroyan,
　　Oh, open the door to me!

"Dinna ye mind, love Gregory,
　　As we sat at the wine,
We changed the rings frae our fingers,
　　And I can show thee thine.

"Now open the door, love Gregory,
　　Open the door, I pray,
For thy young son is in my arms,
　　And will be dead e'er day."

"Ye lie, ye lie, ye ill woman,
　　So loud I hear ye lie,
For Annie of Lochroyan
　　Is far out owre the sea."

Fair Annie turned her round about,
    "Well, sine that it be so,
May never woman that has born a son
    Hae a heart so full o' woe!

"Tak down, tak down that mast o' gold,
    Set up a mast o' tree,
It disna become a forsaken lady
    To sail so royallie."

When the cock had crawn and the day did dawn
    And the sun began to peep,
Up then raise Lord Gregory
    And sair, sair did he weep.

"Oh, I hae dreamed a dream, Mother,
    I wish it may bring good,
That the bonny lass of Lochroyan
    At my bower window stood."

"Gin it be for Annie of Lochroyan
    That ye mak a' this mane,
She stood last night at your bower door
    But I hae sent her hame."

"Oh, wae betide ye, ill woman,
    An ill death may ye dee!
That wadna open the door yoursel'
    Nor yet wad waken me!"

Oh, he's gane down to yon shore side,
    As fast as he could dree,

And there he saw fair Annie's bark
    A-rowin' owre the sea.

"Oh, Annie, Annie!" loud he cried,
    "Oh, Annie, Annie, bide!"
But aye the louder did he call,
    The broader grew the tide.

The wind blew loud, the waves rose high
    And dashed the boat on shore,
Fair Annie's corpse was in the foam,
    The babe rose never more.

Oh, cherry, cherry was her cheek,
    And gowden was her hair,
And coral, coral was her lips,
    Nane might wi' her compare.

"Oh, wae betide my ill mother,
    An ill death may she dee,
That turned my true love frae my door,
    Who came so far to me!"

Then he's ta'en out a little dart,
    Hung low down by his gore,
He thrust it through and through his heart,
    And words spake never more.

The Holy Well

AN OLD ENGLISH BALLAD

It fell out one May morning,
　　On a bright holiday,
Sweet Jesus asked of his dear mother
　　If he might go to play.

"To play, to play, sweet Jesus shall go,
　　And to play pray get you gone,
And let me hear of no complaint
　　At night when you come home."

Sweet Jesus went down in yonder town,
　　As far as the Holy Well,
And there he saw as fine children
　　As any tongue can tell.

He said, "God bless you, every one,
　　And your bodies Christ save and see;
Little children, shall I play with you,
　　And you shall play with me."

But they made answer to him, "No."
　　They were lords and ladies all,
And he was but a maiden's child,
　　Born in an ox's stall.

Sweet Jesus turned him about,
　　And he neither spake nor smiled,

But the tears came trickling from his eyes,
  To be but a maiden's child.

Sweet Jesus turned him about,
  To his mother's dear home went he,
And he said, "I've been down in yonder town,
  As far as you can see.

"I've been down in yonder town,
  As far as the Holy Well,
And there I met as fine children,
  As any tongue can tell.

"I said, 'God bless you every one,
  And your bodies Christ save and see,
Little children, shall I play with you,
  And you shall play with me.'

"But they made answer to me, 'No!'
  They were lords and ladies all,
And I was but a maiden's son,
  Born in an ox's stall."

"Though thou art but a maiden's son,
  Born in an ox's stall,
Thou art the Christ, the King of Heaven,
  The master of men all.

"Sweet Jesus, go down in yonder town,
  As far as the Holy Well,
And take away those sinful souls
  And plunge them deep in Hell."

"Nay, nay," sweet Jesus said,
  "Nay, nay, that may not be.
There are too many sinful souls,
  Crying out for the love of me."

Sir Arthur and
Charming Mollee

AN OLD ENGLISH BALLAD

As noble Sir Arthur one morning did ride,
  With his hounds at his feet and his sword at his side,
He saw a fair maid, sitting under a tree.
  He asked her name and she said 'twas Mollee.

"Oh, charming Mollee, you my butler shall be,
  To draw the red wine for yourself and for me.
I'll make you a lady so high in degree,
  If you will but love me, my charming Mollee!

"I'll give you fine ribbons, I'll give you fine rings,
  I'll give you fine jewels and many fine things.
I'll give you a petticoat, flounced to the knee,
  If you will but love me, my charming Mollee!"

"I'll have none of your ribbons and none of your rings,
  And none of your jewels and other fine things.
And I've got a petticoat, suits my degree,
  And I'll ne'er love a married man, till his wife dee."

"Oh, charming Mollee, give me then your penknife,
  And I will go home and I'll kill my own wife,
I'll kill my own wife and my children three,
  If you will but love me, my charming Mollee!"

"Oh, noble Sir Arthur, it must not be so.
  Go home to your wife and let nobody know.

For seven long years I'll wait then for thee,
    But I'll ne'er love a married man, till his wife dee."

So the seven long years are gone and are past,
    And the old woman went to her long home at last;
The old woman died and Sir Arthur was free,
    And he soon came a-courting to charming Mollee.

Now charming Mollee in her carriage doth ride,
    With her hounds at her feet and her lord at her side.
Oh, all you fair maids, take a warning by me,
    And ne'er love a married man—till his wife dee!

Cupid's Garden

As I were in Cupid's garden,
    No more nor half an hour,
'twas there I seed two maidens,
    Sitting under Cupid's bower,

A-gathering of sweet jasmine,
    The lily and the rose.
These be the fairest flowers
    As in the garden grows.

I proudly stepped to one of them,
    And unto her I says,
"Be ye engaged to arra young man?
    Now tell to me, I prays."

"I bean't engaged to narra young man,
    I solemnly declare.
I aims to live a maiden
    And aye the laurel wear."

Says I, "My stars and garters!
    That this should e'er be so!
For as fine a young maid as ever was,
    To treat all mankind so!"

But t'other young maid looked sly at me,
  And from her seat she's risen.
Says she, "Let thee and I go our own way,
  And we'll let she go shis'n."

The Divided Horsecloth

AN OLD FRENCH FABLIAU

BERNIER

Twelfth Century

There dwelt in Paris a rich merchant who desired to
make for his son a fair marriage in an honorable house.
So he sought for him a bride of birth and breeding, the
daughter of a noble knight who had lost his heritage.

And the knight said, "Certes, Sir Merchant, this
marriage cannot be agreed upon unless you grant to
your son the sum and total of your substance, so that he
be possessed of all your wealth. If you consent to this
the marriage can be made."

The merchant turned this over for a while, looking
at his son. At last he made reply. "My lord, it shall be
done according to your will. I take this company to
witness that here I strip myself of everything I own. I
grant my son all that I have of worth."

So the son and the lady were wed and a fair child
was born to them and they loved and cherished him
fondly. Now the old merchant was full of years and he
was bent with age, as one who searches for his lost youth.
His son grew weary of his presence and the dame held
him in utter despite. Never was she silent, but always
was she saying to her lord,

"Husband, for love of me send your father upon his

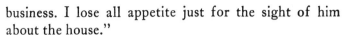
business. I lose all appetite just for the sight of him about the house."

"Wife," he said, "it shall be done according to your wish." So he sought out his father and he said to him, "Father, get you gone from here. For twelve years and more we have given you food and raiment in our house. Now all is done, so rise and depart forthwith and fend for yourself, as fend you must."

When the father heard these words he wept bitterly. "Ah, fair sweet son, for the love of God turn me not from thy door. I require from thee neither seat in the chimney corner, nor soft bed of feathers, no, nor carpet on the floor. But only the attic, where I may bide on a little straw. Throw me not from thy house, because I eat thy bread, but feed me the short time I have to live."

"Fair father," replied the son, "get you forth at once."

"Fair son, where then shall I go?"

"Get you to the town. Seek your fortune bravely. Perchance some of your friends will receive you into their house. But go you must, because it is according to my will."

Then the father grieved so bitterly that his very heart would have broken. "Son," he said, "I commend you to God. But since thou wilt that I go, for the love of Him give me at least a portion of packing cloth to shelter me against the wind. I am lightly clad and fear to die by reason of the cold."

"Father, I have no cloth that I can have taken from me."

"Fair sweet son, give me then the cloth that you

spread upon your horse, so that I come to no evil."

Then he, seeing that he might not rid himself of his father save by the granting of a gift, called his son and said to the lad, "Fair son, get you to the stable and give my father the covering that is upon my horse."

Then the lad made answer, "Grandsire, come with me." And when they were come to the stable he chose the best horse cloth that he might find. This he folded in two and drawing forth his knife he cut the cloth into two portions and bestowed on his grandfather one half the sundered horsecloth.

"Fair child," cried the old man, "what have you done? Why have you cut the cloth your father hath given me? Very cruelly have you treated me." And he returned to the house and said, "Son, chastize now thy child! Dost thou see that he keeps one half of the horsecloth?"

"Plague take thee," cried the father, "give him all the cloth."

"Certes," said the boy, "that will I never do, for how then shall you be paid? Rather will I keep the half until I am a grown man and then give it to you. For just as you have chased him from your house so will I put you out of my door. Naught shall you have of me save only what you have granted to him. If you leave him to die in his misery I will wait my day and surely will leave you to perish in yours."

The father listened to these words. And after a long while he turned to the merchant and said, "Father, return to my house. You are master and lord and I render all that I have received into your hands. Chimney corner and carpet, pillow and bed of feathers, at your ease you shall have pleasure in them all. Henceforth you shall live softly near a blazing fire, clad in your furred robe, even as I. And all this is not of charity, but of your right, for, fair sweet Father, if I am rich it is because of your substance."

Thus the brave dealing of a child freed this father from the bad thoughts he harbored. And deeply should this be considered by those who are about to marry off their children. Let them not strip themselves so bare as to have nothing left. For he who gives all and depends upon the charity of others prepares a rod for his own back.

The Romance
of
Tristram and Iseult

So please you, gentles, I will tell a fair tale of love and death. It is the tale of Tristram and of Iseult, the Queen. Listen, how with great joy and great grief they loved each other and died on the same day.

Ye know how Tristram carried Iseult from the shores of Ireland and bare her to Cornwall, to be the bride of King Mark. And ye know how Iseult's mother had brewed a magic potion and given it secretly unto Bragwaine, who was Iseult's waiting woman, saying to her,

"When King Mark and Queen Iseult are wed, pour this wine into a cup and bid them drink together, for such is its virtue that they who drink will love each other with all their senses forever, in life and death."

Now on a day, when the ship bare them across the sea, Tristram came to Iseult and strove to calm the anger in her heart. The sun was shining and they were athirst and they asked for drink. And, because Bragwaine was not there, a little serving wench sought for wine and found a phial. "I have found wine," she said. But no, it was not wine. It was passion and bitter joy and anguish without end and death. Iseult took the goblet and she drank a deep draught and she handed it to Tristram and he drained the cup.

Then Bragwaine entered and saw how they gazed at each other in silence, ravished and amazed. She saw the empty phial and the goblet, and she cried out, "Alas, cursed be the day that I was born! Iseult, my dear one, and you, Tristram, it is death that ye have drunk."

And it seemed to Tristram that a strong briar, with sharp roots and scented flowers was striking its roots into the blood of his heart, and binding his body and all his thoughts and all his desires with strong ligaments to the fair body of Iseult.

And he gazed upon Iseult and heard her say, "Alas, why have I left the country of my birth? What sail I to Tintagel, to King Mark?"

And Tristram whispered, "Iseult, what is it grieves thee?"

"Ah, all that I know grieves me! The sky above me and the sea around and my body and my life." Then she laid her arm on Tristram's shoulder and tears quenched the brightness of her eyes.

And Tristram said, "Iseult, what is it tortures thee?"

She answered, "The love of thee."

Then he pressed his lips to hers and Bragwaine fell upon her knees and said, "Dear Tristram, dear Iseult, alas, I offer ye my body and my life in atonement for the evil guard I kept. For by my fault ye drank love and death from the accursed cup."

And Tristram answered, "Then come death!"

When night fell they were bound forever and the ship bare them swiftly to the country of King Mark.

In due course King Mark took Iseult to wife. And Tristram left the country and wandered over many lands, doing deeds of prowess. And after two years the Duke of Brittany said to him.

"Sir, I would pay my debt to you. Behold my daughter, Iseult of the White Hands. Take her to wife."

Now Tristram was weary and her name was as music in his ears, so he said, "Sir, I will take her." But after they were wed he told her that he had made a vow to God that he would not embrace a woman, no, not his wife, for a whole year. And so was Tristram true to his beloved, to Iseult the Queen.

Now, gentles, ye shall hear a dolorous tale. It fell that in a battle Tristram was wounded with a poisoned lance. He lay in his castle in Brittany and the wise men sought to heal his wound, and Tristram's heart was far across the sea. Then he sent a friend, Kaherdin the Faithful, to take his ring unto Iseult the Fair.

"Tell her if she comes not I shall die. Let her remember the philtre we drank together on the sea. Ah, it was death we drank. Take my fair ship and say to Iseult of the White Hands that you go in search of a leech. Take with you two sails, one white, the other black. If you bring Iseult the Queen hoist the white sail when you return. If you bring her not, then raise the black. Friend, I have no more to say. God keep you safe."

Then Tristram fell back upon his bed and Kaherdin wept and departed to bring Iseult the Fair. But Iseult of the White Hands had stood outside the door. She had heard that he loved another. She heard, and she remembered.

Kaherdin sailed with all the speed he might to the port of Tintagel. There he disguised him as a merchant and took his wares to the palace and showed them to the queen. And he drew Tristram's ring from his finger and laid it beside the other wares. When Iseult saw the jasper ring her heart beat and her color changed.

Kaherdin said quickly, "Lady, Tristram lies wounded by a poisoned blade. He is nigh to death. Keep the ring. He sends it to you."

Iseult answered, "Friend, I will follow you. Let your ship sail in the night." Then she looked across the sea and said, "God grant, beloved, either that I heal thee or that we both die of the same pang."

And all this time Tristram languished. Each day he sent to see if the vessel were in sight and of what color was the sail. As long as the sun showed above the horizon he looked out to sea and at night he lay upon his couch and thought only of Iseult the Queen, who came not.

At last the ship with the white sail was near at hand, but Tristram was too weak to see it. And then Iseult of the White Hands avenged herself. She came to Tristram's bedside and she said,

"Beloved, Kaherdin comes. I have seen his ship on the sea. May it bring you healing."

Tristram trembled and he said, "Fair wife, tell me, what like is the sail?"

"I saw it well. They have hoisted it high and spread it wide. It is all black."

Then Tristram turned his face to the wall. He repeated thrice, "Iseult, beloved!" And the fourth time he died.

Now the ship with the white sail had come to land.

Iseult the Fair made what speed she might to the shore. She heard the wailing in the streets. She heard and could not speak. She went up to the palace and the Bretons marvelled as she passed, for never had they seen so fair a lady. Iseult of the White Hands grieved for the evil she had wrought and wept over Tristram's body.

Iseult the Fair entered and said, "Lady, rise, and let me come near. I have a greater right to weep for him than you. I loved him more."

She turned toward the East and prayed to God. Then she lay down beside her lover and kissed him on the lips and clasped him closely in her arms, mouth to mouth and body to body. And so she died.

Gentles, the good trouveres of olden times have told this tale for all those who love. And not for others.

Griselda

BOCCACCIO

1313–1375

The Lord of Saluzzo took to wife Griselda, the daughter of a peasant. And after she had born two children to him he was minded to make trial of her patience, and he told her that his vassals were ill-content that she, who had been a tender of sheep, should bear his children. And he sent a serving man to take the boy and girl from her, and let her think they should be put to death.

And Griselda said, "Take them! And do what thy lord hath enjoined! That which pleaseth him who begot them pleaseth me, also. Only leave them not to be devoured of the beasts and the birds—except he command it of thee."

Then her lord despatched the children privily to one who should bring them up in secret.

And when twelve years were gone he made of Griselda's patience the supreme trial. He told her that he purposed to put her away and take another wife.

And Griselda said, "All that you have given me I have accounted but a loan. It pleaseth you to require it again and it must and doth content me to restore it you. Here is your ring wherewith you espoused me."

And her lord said, "I would have thee prepare the house and nuptial festival for my new bride."

And Griselda said, "I am ready and willing. I will receive thy bride."

Then the Lord of Saluzzo let bring his daughter, who was now fourteen years old and very fair and he made a feast and festival and he told his guests that the young maid was come to be his wife.

And he summonded Griselda from ordering the chambers and preparing the viands and he said, "Go and meet my bride."

And Griselda said, "Even that will I do, my lord." And she greeted the maiden, whom she knew not for her daughter, and she said, "Welcome and fair welcome to my lady." And she said, "My lord, I think you will live the happiest gentleman in the world with her. But I beseech you, as most I may, that you inflict not on her those things that you inflicted on her who was sometime yours. She is young, my lord, and I think she might scarce avail to endure them."

And her lord said, "Griselda, take her whom thou deemest my bride, and her brother, for thy children and mine. And know that I am thy lord, who loveth thee above all else."

And he kissed her and brought her children to her. And so did Griselda reap the fruit of her long patience.

Peronella

BOCCACCIO

There was a wife called Peronella, who was mightily in love with a young gallant of the neighborhood. One morning, her husband having gone to work, she and her gallant were together, and her husband returned home before his time and finding the door locked, knocked thereon.

Peronella said, "Alack, Gianello mine, I am a dead woman! Here is my husband and I know not what this meaneth, for he never was come back hither at this hour. For the love of God, get thee into yonder vat and hide, whilst I go and open to him."

Gianello betook himself with all haste into the vat and Peronella said, "What is now to do, husband, that thou returnest home so soon?"

And her husband said, "Good wife, I have sold to yonder man that thou seest here with me the vat that hath this long time cumbered the house. He will give me five lily florins for it and he is come to carry it away."

"Oh!" said Peronella. "He is come to carry it away?"

"Aye," said her husband, "he is come to carry it away. Do but stand aside, good wife, that he may take it."

"Now," said Peronella, "I will show thee how careful I have been of thy welfare, for I have sold the vat for seven florins to an honest man who entered it but now to see if it were sound."

Then the husband was well pleased and he sent away the man who would have given him but five and he said, "Where is now this man who will give me seven?"

Then Gianello, who had abode all this while with his ears pricked up, scrambled out of the vat and Peronella said, "Lo, there he comes. And he finds it all encrusted with lime. He will not take it unless first he sees it clean. Come, good man, here is my husband. He will clean it out for thee. Here, husband, here is a light and a scraper. Enter the vat and fall a-scraping and see that it be clean and smooth."

And so long as they heard him scraping did she and her gallant kiss each other in all sweetness and content. And when she heard him silent would Peronella thrust her head in at the mouth of the vat and cry, "Scrape here! There, also. See, there is yet a little left." And again, so long as the good man was busy with his scraper, were she and her gallant busy with their affairs.

And when the vat was clean Gianello gave the husband seven florins for it and let carry the vat to his own house.

And Peronella said, "God speed, good man! And may the vat still serve thee well! Husband mine, art thou not content with my morning's work? Thou seest, thy wife knows how to keep her wits about her. Thou needest have no fear but I will always deal so with thee, under the governance of love!"

Madam Catalina

BOCCACCIO

There was a gentleman called Gentile Carisendi who was enamored of a lady called Madam Catalina, but because she was virtuous and steadfast in love to her husband Messer Gentile left the city in despair. And while he was absent he had word that Madam Catalina had been stricken with a grievous sickness and lay dead and that she had been buried in a vault in the churchyard.

And Messer Gentile said, "Ah, Madam Catalina, thou art dead, thou of whom while thou livedst I could never avail to have so much as a look. Now thou canst not defend thyself needs must I take of thee a kiss or two, all dead as thou art."

Then it being presently night, he mounted a horse and rode till he came where the lady was buried. And he entered the churchyard and came to the sepulchre and opened it with a wrenching iron and went therein. And he saw the lady, lying on a bier. He set down his torch and laid himself beside her, and putting his face to hers he kissed her with many tears.

But presently he feared that the morning was at hand and he bethought himself to tarry in the womb of death no longer. And he said, "Ere I leave her I would touch her on the breast. I have never done so, nor may I ever touch her more."

He put his hand into her bosom and him seemed he felt her heart beat somewhat. And he lay close to her and knew she was not dead. Then he recalled the strayed life to the lady until she raised her eyes and knew him. And when she would have cried aloud she looked about her and apprehended where she was. And she lay silent.

Then Messer Gentile brought her forth from the tomb and closed the sepulchre and carried her privily to his own house. And his mother tended her right lovingly, till after certain weeks she was healed of her illness.

Then Messer Gentile let prepare a banquet and he bade many gentlemen of the city, among whom was the lady's husband. And when the repast was near its end he said, "Gentlemen, you have honored me with your presence and I mean to honor you by showing you the most precious thing I have or ever may have in the world."

Then two of his servants let draw the curtains and the lady came into the room, magnificently dressed and adorned, and Messer Gentile received her.

Her husband rose up and looked at her, as she were a wraith, and indeed him seemed she must be so. And Messer Gentile said, "Madam, comfort your husband, that he may believe his fortune. We will tell him how these things came to pass." And when he saw her go to her lord's embrace he said, "So, I return to you the thing most precious in the world, that I have never touched, save in the darkness of a tomb."

Chichibio

BOCCACCIO

Currado Gianfigliazzi one day brought down a crane and sent it to his cook to roast for supper. When it was all but done a wench of the neighborhood entered the kitchen and said,

"Chichibio, give me a thigh thereof. Give me a thigh thereof, ere I die of longing for this savory smell. Ah, Chichibio, do this, and thou shalt have of me that which will pleasure thee!"

So the cook, who was but a foolish wight and easily cozened by a pair of black eyes, cut off one of the thighs of the crane and gave it her.

Now when the bird was served to his master and certain guests the master said, "Chichibio, what has come of the other thigh?"

Whereupon the cook made answer, "Sir, cranes have but one thigh and one leg."

"What the devil!" cried his master. "They have but one thigh and one leg! Have I never seen a crane before?"

"Sir," replied Chichibio, "it is as I tell you, and when it pleaseth you I will cause you to see it in the quick."

"Then I desire to see it tomorrow morning, in which case I shall be content. But by Christ, His faith, an it be otherwise I will have thee served in such a manner that thou wilt remember as long as thou livest!"

35

The next morning the master, whose anger was nothing abated for sleep, arose full of wrath and bade them bring the horses for himself and Chichibio.

"Now we shall see who lied yestereve, thou or I!"

Chichibio, knowing that he must make good his lie, rode after his master in the greatest fright that might be. He looked all about him and took all that he saw for cranes standing on two feet. Presently they came to a river bank and he saw a round dozen of cranes, all perched on one leg, as they do when they sleep.

Whereupon he cried, "Now, sir, if you will look yonder, you will see that I spoke the truth yesternight, to wit, that cranes have but one thigh and one leg."

"Wait and I will show thee that they have two," said the master, and he shouted out, "Ho! Ho!" At this, the cranes, putting down the other leg, after some steps took to flight. "How sayest thou now, malapert knave that thou art? Deemest thou now that they have two legs?"

And Chichibio, all a-tremble and knowing not whether he stood on his head or his heels, made answer, "Aye, sir, but you did not cry Ho! Ho! to yesternight's crane! Had you cried this, it would have put down the other leg, even as did those yonder."

Ghismonda

BOCCACCIO

Tancred, the Lord of Salerno, had a daughter, Ghismonda, who was fair of form and favor as ever woman was, and whom he loved so tenderly that he kept her closely by him at his court.

And Ghismonda looked upon a young waiting man, Guiscardo, and he pleased her and she him, in such wise that their minds were diverted from well nigh everything other than the thought of love. And after they had tendered their love in secret for a time Ghismonda made it known to him how he should come privily into her garden of a night. And they greeted one another with marvelous great joy and were together then and many times thereafter. And their fellowship, for all that it must abide secret, became a very fair and lovesome thing.

But fortune was jealous of so long and great delight. It fell that the lovers, all unknowing, were seen of Tancred. And the next day he caused Guiscardo to be taken and thrown into a cell. Then he went to his daughter's chamber and told her what he had seen and what he had done—and what he purposed.

And Ghismonda made no outcry nor tears, as women mostly do, but she spake as one undaunted and valiant. "Tancred, I purpose neither to deny nor to entreat. True it is that I have loved and love Guiscardo, and

that while I live, which will be little, I shall love him, nor
if folk live after death shall I ever leave loving him. I
am minded to proffer no prayer, for I see it would not
move thee. Begone! Shed tears with women! And then
slay him and me with the same blow, an it seem to thee
we have deserved it."

Tancred went from her and that night he bade the
jailor slay Guiscardo and bring his heart to him. And
when it was done he set the heart in a great and goodly
bowl of gold and he despatched it to his daughter by
a privy servant, bidding him say, "Thy father sendeth
thee this to solace thee of the thing that most thou
lovest."

When Ghismonda heard this she took the cup with a
steadfast countenance and uncovered it. She saw the
heart and apprehended the words of the message and
turning her eyes upon the messenger she said to him,
"No sepulchre less of worth than one of gold had be-
seemed this heart, and in this hath my father done
discreetly. Still in everything, and to this extreme limit
of my life, have I found his love most tender to me.
Wherefore do thou render him for so great a gift the
last thanks I shall ever have to give him."

And when the man had gone she took a vial of poison
and she poured the poison into a bowl and she kissed the
heart and bowed her head and wept.

"Oh, much loved heart, I have accomplished mine
every office to thee. Nor is there left me ought else to do,
save to come with my soul and bear thine company."

Then she raised the bowl and drank the poison and
her tears, and having drunken she mounted upon the

bed and she pressed her dead lover's heart to her own and laid her down.

Then her women, albeit they knew not what water she had drunk, sent to tell the prince. He came quickly to her chamber and when he saw her extremity he fell a-weeping grievously.

And the lady said, "Tancred, keep these tears against a less desired fate than mine. Give them not to me, who need them not. Nevertheless, if ought yet live in thee of the love that once thou borest me, vouchsafe me for a last boon that, since it was not thy pleasure that I should in secret live with Guiscardo, my body may openly abide with his, wherever thou hast cast him, dead." Then she held the dead heart to her breast and she said, "Abide ye with God, for I go hence."

Tancred, too late repenting him, caused them to be buried in one sepulchre. Such was the ending of so great a love.

A Strange Love

GUY DE MAUPASSANT

1850–1893

The Marquis de Bertrans was giving a dinner at the opening of the hunting season. He and his guests were sitting at a candle-lit table, covered with fruits and flowers, and they were discussing love. It was the eternal argument, whether one could love once or many times, whether it was a great single passion that fell like a thunderbolt from heaven or whether one could love often, each time with all his strength and soul. The doctor of the neighborhood was chosen as arbitrator and he said,

"I have known of one passion that lasted for fifty-five years without a day of respite and that was ended only by death."

The Marquise clapped her hands. "How beautiful! How happy the woman must be who is adored like that!"

The doctor laughed. "Ah, but madame, the one loved was a man. You know him. It is Monsieur Chouquet, the village pharmacist. As for the woman, you knew her, too. She was the old woman who put cane seats in chairs. When she was dying she told me her story. I heard all about her ragged and uncared-for childhood and how her parents used to send her around to collect the worn-out chairs to be re-bottomed. One day, when she was about eleven years old, she met the little Chouquet crying because he had lost two sous. She couldn't bear to see this little well-to-do citizen crying. She thought he was one of the fortunate ones who should always be happy. So she went up to him and poured into his hands all her savings, seven sous. He took them. And then, in a frenzy of joy and excitement, she embraced him. As he was counting the money attentively he allowed her to do so. And then she ran away.

"For months she dreamed of the boy. She watched him on the streets, playing marbles with his friends. Once she kissed him again, and when he was angry she gave him her savings to appease him. He took the money and let her caress him as much as she wished. During the next few years she gave him all she could. She thought of nothing but him. She used to stand outside his father's druggist shop and watch him, between a great bottle of red colored liquid and a tape worm.

"You who understand love—do you know why she attached herself to this booby? Was it because she had sacrificed her vagabond fortune for him, or because she had given him her first tender kiss? The mystery is the same for the small as for the great, is it not?

"Then he went away to school and college and when he came back she used to pass him without daring to speak. He never deigned to look at her and she had no longer the courage to raise her eyes to his. One night, soon after he married, she threw herself into the pond, but she was dragged out and taken to the pharmacy. Young Chouquet himself had to come down in his dressing gown and care for her. But all he said was, 'Why do you make a beast of yourself like this?'

"The years passed and he never spoke to her again, except when she forced herself to go into the pharmacy and buy a few things, so that she could be near him for a minute or two and still give him a little money.

"She said to me, 'Doctor, he is the only man I have seen on earth. I have not known that there are others existing.'

"Well, she died last spring. She asked me to give all her savings to the man she had loved. 'I have worked only for him, Doctor,' she said. 'I went without food often in order to save. I wanted to be sure that he would think of me at least once, after I am gone.'

"After I had paid for her burial I took her savings—they amounted to a little over two thousand francs—and I went around to the Chouquets'. They had just finished supper and they were sitting opposite each other, very important and satisfied. They made me be seated and gave me a liqueur and I began my story. I thought they would be profoundly moved, but when they understood that he had been loved by this vagabond, this chair mender, Chouquet fairly bounced with indignation. It was as though she had robbed him of his reputation. His wife kept repeating, 'The beggar, the beggar, the beggar!' She couldn't seem to find another word. Chouquet got up and walked around with long strides. 'Think of it, doctor!' he said. 'The insult! The humiliation! If I had known this while she was alive I would have had her arrested and shut up in prison.'

"I was stunned. I didn't know what to say or do, but

I had to complete my mission, so I said, 'She charged me to give you her savings, which amount to about two thousand francs. But since what I have told you seems so very disagreeable to you, perhaps it would be better to give the money to the poor.'

"I wish you could have seen their faces. They looked at me, stupefied from shock. Madame Chouquet found her voice first. 'Well, since it was the last wish of this— person, it seems to me that it would be very difficult to refuse.'

" 'Exactly!' said Chouquet. 'Exactly! And besides, we could always buy something with it for the children.'

" 'As you wish,' I said drily.

" 'Yes,' he said, 'give it to me! Give it to me! You may be sure that we shall find the means of using it in some good work.'

"I laid the money on the table and bowed and went out.

"The next day Chouquet came to me and bowed and said brusquely, 'She must have left a wagon, that woman. What are you going to do with it?'

" 'Nothing,' I said. 'Take it, if you like.'

" 'It's just what I want. I will make a lean-to of it for my kitchen.'

"Well, the wagon serves Chouquet as a lean-to and he has bought railroad bonds with the money. And that, my friends, is the only profound love I ever knew in my life!"

How He Won the Legion of Honor

GUY DE MAUPASSANT

Ever since he was a child Monsieur Caillard had had but one idea in his head, and that was to win the Legion of Honor. There didn't seem much likelihood of it, for as a boy and a young man he had failed in all his studies and examinations. So, not knowing what else to do, he had married a pretty girl, with plenty of money of her own. But he still kept on thinking about the Legion of Honor.

Sometimes, when he was walking along the street, he would count the decorations as he passed them. "Just let me see how many I shall meet between the Madeleine and the Rue Drouot." Then he would walk slowly, looking at every coat for the little bit of red ribbon, and he would say, "Eight officers and ten knights. As many as that! It's stupid to sow the ribbon broadcast like that. I wonder how many I shall meet going back." He used to imagine himself walking gravely in a procession, his crush hat under his arm, his breast covered with medals, radiant as a star. But, alas, he had no right to wear any decoration whatever!

Finally he spoke to his wife about it and she was stupefied. "Decorated!" she said. "But what on earth have you done to deserve it?"

44

He got angry at that. "I know what I'm talking about. Really, you are a very stupid woman sometimes."

Then he asked her to speak about it to Rosselin, the Deputy, who had the Legion of Honor, though no one knew exactly why. "Just ask him how one goes about getting it," said Monsieur Caillard. "I can't very well broach the subject, but coming from you it might seem quite natural."

The Deputy was a little vague about it. He said that perhaps if Monsieur Caillard wrote some things worthy of distinction—perhaps—who knows—

So Monsieur Caillard started to write. He began a pamphlet on The People's Right to Instruction, but could not finish it for want of ideas. Then he produced one on The Education of Children by Means of the Eye. He had this printed and sent a copy to each Deputy, ten to each Minister and fifty to the President of the Republic. Then he wrote one on The Sources of Human Knowledge and one on Street Lending Libraries. He sent the tracts all over, to every newspaper and dozens to every officer of the Government. They attracted no attention at all.

He was encouraged, however, because Monsieur Rosselin, the Deputy, seemed all at once to take a great interest in his success.

He came constantly to the house and offered a lot of sound practical advice. One day he said to him, "Caillard, I have just obtained a great favor for you. The Committee on Historical Documents is going to send you on a commission. They will allow you to make some researches in the various provincial libraries of France."

Monsieur Caillard was so delighted that he could scarcely eat or drink. And a week later he set out.

After he had been gone for two weeks, traveling from town to town and being a bore to all the librarians, he found himself at Rouen and he thought that as he was so near Paris he would like to embrace his wife. So he took the nine o'clock train, reached his home by midnight and let himself in with his latchkey, overjoyed at the thought of the surprise he was going to give her.

He went quietly upstairs and found her bedroom door locked. How tiresome! But he knocked and called, "Jeanne, it is I!"

She must have been very much surprised. He heard her jump out of bed and then she seemed to be speaking aloud to herself! Then she went to her dressing room, opened and closed the door and ran quickly up and down her room several times. At last she asked, "Is it you Alexandre?" She opened the door and threw hersel into his arms. "Oh, what a fright you gave me! What surprise! What a pleasure! What a joy to have yo home!"

After he had kissed her he began to undress methoc ically. He picked up the overcoat from a chair and sud denly he stood motionless, struck dumb. There was a red ribbon in the buttonhole!

"Why," he stammered, "this overcoat has the rosette in it."

His wife caught it from his hands. "No! No, no! You've made a mistake. Give it to me."

Monsieur Caillard repeated in a daze. "But whose

overcoat is it? It's not mine. It has the Legion of Honor on it."

His wife seemed terrified, but she said, "Listen, give it to me—I mustn't tell you—it's a secret—"

Monsieur Caillard grew pale. "I want to know how this overcoat comes here. It doesn't belong to me."

Then she almost screamed at him, "Yes, it does! Listen, I oughtn't to tell you—it's supposed to be a secret but, well, you're decorated!"

Monsieur Caillard dropped into a chair. "Decorated!"

"Yes, but it's a secret, a great secret." She put the glorious garment into a cupboard and came to her husband, pale and trembling. "It's a new overcoat that I had made for you. But I swore I wouldn't say anything about it—for it won't be announced for a month or so. Monsieur Rosselin managed it for you."

"Rosselin!" Monsieur Caillard could scarcely speak for joy. "He got the decoration for me!"

"It looks so, doesn't it?" said his wife.

A little white card had fallen to the floor out of a pocket of the overcoat. Monsieur Caillard picked it up and read it. It was a visiting card and it said, "Rosselin, Deputy."

His wife looked at it and smiled. "You see how it is," she said.

A few weeks later it was announced in the Journal Officiel that Monsieur Caillard had been awarded the Legion of Honor, "on account of his exceptional services."

Regret

GUY DE MAUPASSANT

It was a dull autumn day and the leaves were falling. They fell quietly in the rain, resembling another rain, but heavier and slower. Monsieur Savel stood looking out of the window, thinking over his empty life. He was sixty-two, an old bachelor, alone in the world, with no one to care for him. He pondered over his life, so barren and so void. He had not even known the ecstasy of a triumphant passion.

Ah, but he had been in love! He had loved Madame Saudres, the wife of his old companion, Saudres. He recalled the long evenings in their home when she was young and beautiful, the walks the three of them used to take along the Seine and the lunches on the grass on Sundays. He remembered one afternoon when Saudres had gone to sleep on his back after lunch and he and Madame Saudres had walked along the river bank together.

She had leaned tenderly on his arm and smiled up at him and he had felt himself grow pale and hoped the trembling of his hands did not betray him. She had decked herself with wild flowers and she had asked him,

"Do you like to see me this way? Do you like me with flowers in my hair?"

And when he did not answer, for he dared not, she

had said, "Great goose, what's the matter with you? You might at least say something!"

As they walked along he had felt her ear against his cheek and he had tilted his head abruptly, for fear she had not meant to bring their flesh into contact.

At last he said, "Well—is it not time to return?"

And she had answered, "Just as you like, my friend. You're tired, are you? Oh, very well, if you find the walk too long by all means let's return!"

But on their way back she had been silent and had leaned no longer on his arm. And now, after more than thirty years, Monsieur Savel looked out at the dull autumn rain and wondered why.

Suddenly he jumped up and put on his coat. "I must ask her. I must know what she meant. I am sixty-two and she is fifty-eight. Surely I may ask her now without giving offence!"

He went out into the rain and hurried along to the Saudres' house and knocked. A little servant opened the door and Monsieur Savel said, "Good morning, my girl, good morning! Will you tell your mistress, please, that I should like to see her at once?"

"But, Monsieur Savel, madame is preparing the pear jam for the winter. She is standing in front of the fire. Madame is not dressed to receive, as monsieur may well understand."

"That doesn't matter," said Monsieur Savel. "It is important that I should see her at once. Please go and tell her, my girl."

The little servant went off and Monsieur Savel began to walk up and down the room with long nervous strides.

At last the door opened and madame appeared. She was now a big woman, round and fat, with red cheeks and a hearty laugh. She walked with her arms held away from her body. Her sleeves were tucked up to her elbows and her bare arms were all smeared with sugar juice.

"Well," she said, "good morning, my friend. What's the matter? You're not ill, are you?"

"No, but I must ask you something that is torturing my heart. Will you answer me truthfully?"

"I am always truthful. What is it?"

"Well, then, I have loved you from the first day I ever saw you. You don't doubt me, do you?"

"You great goose! What's the matter with you? I've known it from the very first day."

Monsieur Savel began to tremble. He stammered, "You knew it! Then—then what—"

She began to laugh. "Then? What?"

"What—what would you have answered?"

She broke into a peal of laughter that made the sugar juice run off the tips of her fingers onto the carpet. "Answered? I? But you didn't ask me anything. It wasn't for me to speak."

"Stop laughing! Do you remember that day when Saudres went to sleep on his back after lunch and you and I walked along the river bank together?"

"That day! Oh, yes, my friend! Yes, I remember that day very well indeed!"

"Well, that day—if I had been enterprising—what would you have answered?"

Then she laughed, as only a happy woman can laugh, who has nothing to regret.

"I would have yielded, my friend." She turned on her heel and went back to her jam making.

Monsieur Savel rushed out into the street and went with giant strides through the rain until he reached the river bank. He went straight on, his clothes running with water, his hat dripping like a crushed rag. At last he came to the place where they had walked together so many, many years ago.

He sat down under the leafless trees and wept.

A Fishing Excursion

GUY DE MAUPASSANT

Paris was blockaded, desolate, famished. Monsieur Morisot was walking along the boulevard one day, sad and hungry, when he came across his old friend and companion, Monsieur Sauvage, who kept a little notion store in the Rue Notre Dame de Lorette. The two old friends used to go fishing together every Sunday, but now, with the war and the Prussians so near the gates of Paris, they had not dared to take an outing for a long time. They went into a café and each took a glass of absinthe and talked about the fishing excursions they used to enjoy so much. The balmy air and a second glass of absinthe made Monsieur Sauvage feel a little reckless and he said,

"It's the first nice day we've had all year. Morisot, let's go fishing."

"But where?" said Monsieur Morisot.

"At our old spot. At Colombes. The French soldiers are stationed near there. I know Colonel Dumoulin will give us a pass."

They hurried home and got their fishing tackle and a couple of hours later they had reached the Colonel's villa and had received a pass in due form. They went on to the advance guard, presented their pass, walked through Colombes and reached their destination. The great plains toward Nanterre were deserted.

"See," said Monsieur Sauvage, "the Prussians are over there."

"What if we should meet some?" said Monsieur Morisot.

"We would ask them to join us," said Monsieur Sauvage, in true Parisian style.

They sat down on the river bank behind some bushes and settled themselves for a good day's sport. The fish came easily to their bait and soon they had forgotten everything—even the war.

Suddenly they heard a rumbling sound and the earth shook beneath them. It was the cannon on Mont Valerien. They looked up and saw a trail of smoke in the sky and heard another explosion.

"They're at it again," said Monsieur Sauvage, shrugging his shoulders.

"Stupid fools," said Monsieur Morisot, "what pleasure can they find in killing each other? They're worse than brutes."

"It will always be thus, as long as we have governments."

"Well, such is life," said Monsieur Morisot.

"You mean—death," said Monsieur Sauvage.

Suddenly they started. They heard a sound behind them. They turned and saw four big men in dark uniforms with guns pointed at them. Their fishing lines dropped out of their hands and floated away with the current.

In a few minutes the Prussians had bound them and rowed them across the river to an island that our friends had thought deserted. A big burly officer, seated astride of a chair and smoking a pipe, addressed them in excellent French.

"Well, gentlemen, have you made a good haul?" A soldier threw on the grass at his feet the net full of fish that the two old friends had caught. "You are evidently sent to spy upon me," said the officer. "You pretend to fish, but I am not so simple. I have caught you and I shall have you shot. I am sorry, but war is war. However— as you passed your advance guard you must have the password. Give it to me and I will set you free."

The two old friends stood side by side. They were pale but they answered nothing.

The Prussian came over to them. "No one will ever know. You will go quietly back home and the secret will disappear with you. If you refuse it is instant death. Choose!"

The two old men were silent.

"In five minutes you'll be at the bottom of that river. Now listen to me. Surely you have friends waiting for you in Paris. You have families, expecting you to come home and sit down with them at the supper table to-night."

The distant cannon rumbled incessantly. The Prussian gave an order and a squad of men advanced to within twenty feet of the prisoners.

"I give you one minute, not a second more." Suddenly he took Monsieur Morisot by the arm and led him aside. "Quick," he whispered, "the password! Your friend won't know. He will think I changed my mind."

Monsieur Morisot said nothing.

The Prussian took Monsieur Sauvage aside and asked him the same thing. He, too, was silent.

The officer gave an order and the squad of men raised their guns. At that moment Monsieur Morisot's eyes rested on the net full of fish lying on the grass. The sight made him a little faint and though he struggled against it his eyes filled with tears. He turned to his old companion.

"Adieu, Monsieur Sauvage!"

"Adieu, Monsieur Morisot!"

"Fire!" said the Prussian.

The squad of men fired as one. Monsieur Sauvage fell straight backwards. Monsieur Morisot swayed and fell across his friend's body, facing the sky. The soldiers tied stones to their feet and threw them into the river. Only a little blood floated to the surface. After a few moments the water flowed calmly once again.

"The fish will get even, now," said the officer. Then he pointed to the net lying on the grass. "Fry these little things while they are still alive. They'll make an excellent meal."

He sat down on his chair and puffed away at his pipe.

The Minuet

GUY DE MAUPASSANT

Jean Bridelle was an old bachelor who passed for a
cynic. He and his friends were talking one evening about
the touching events of life, those little happenings that
enter into one's sympathies like deep unhealable stings.

"Great events move me little," said Jean Bridelle.
"They do not stir me, as do the little wondering sights
of life. I will tell you of one of them.

"Years ago, when I was a young man, I used to go
every morning to walk in a corner of the Luxembourg
Gardens. You would not have known that corner, you
are too young. It was like a forgotten garden of another
century, a lovely garden, like the smile of an old person.
There were flowers and fruit trees and hedges, and calm
walks between walls of foliage, neatly pruned. I used
to sit there and dream and listen to the living Paris all
around me.

"From time to time I saw an old man there. He wore
shoes with silver buckles, lace instead of a cravat, and
an unheard-of hat with the edges badly worn. He carried
a superb cane, with a golden head, which must have been
a souvenir, and a magnificent one. One day I bowed to
him and said, 'It's a fine day, monsieur.' 'Yes, monsieur,'
he replied, 'it reminds me of the weather of the long
ago.'

"A week later we were friends and I knew his history.

56

He had been a dancing master at the opera from the days of Louis XV, and when he began to speak of dancing he never knew when to stop. One day he confided to me, 'I married La Castris, monsieur. If you wish I will present you to her. But she never comes here so early. This garden is our pleasure and our life. It is all that remains to us of former times. Here we seem to breathe an air that has not changed since our youth.'

"Well, you can imagine I went back that afternoon. There was my old friend, giving his arm with great ceremony to a little old woman dressed in black, to whom I was presented. It was La Castris, the great dancer, loved of princes, loved of the king, loved of all that gallant century, which seems to have left in the world the fragrance of love. I bowed over her hand and murmured that I was enchanted, honored.

"She said, 'Thank you, monsieur. It is very good of the men of today to remember the woman of yesterday. Please be seated.'

"We sat down on a bench. I remember that it was in the month of May and the perfume of flowers was all around us. The sun shone between the leaves and the black dress of La Castris seemed all aglow with light. At the end of the allée a young and beautiful woman passed on the arm of a young man. La Castris followed my glance and understood my thought. She smiled a little.

" 'Monsieur,' she murmured, 'it is not possible to be —and to have been—at the same time.'

" 'Life must have been beautiful for you, madame,' I said.

" 'Yes, beautiful and sweet. It is for that that I regret it so much.'

"Her husband began to talk of her successes, her friends, her triumphant existence.

" 'Your greatest joy, then, madame,' I said, 'your deepest happiness, did you owe to the theatre?'

" 'No!' cried La Castris, and the tears came to her eyes. 'You see, monsieur, with most people the heart grows old with the body. With me that has not happened!'

"After a little silence I turned to the old dancing master and spoke at random, because I did not want to see the tears of La Castris. 'Will you tell me, monsieur, what the minuet really was?'

" 'The minuet, monsieur, was the queen of dances and the dance of queens. Since there are no more kings there are no minuets.' He turned to his old companion and said gravely, 'Elise, will you have the kindness to show this gentleman what the minuet really was?'

"She looked at me for a moment without speaking. Then she rose and waited until he took his place opposite her. Then I saw something I shall not forget. Ah, they were old, my friends. You might say it was two old puppets, dancing to an ancient mechanism, a little rusty, a little out of repair. But I seemed to see in it the shadow of a century past and gone.

"They ended the figure of the dance and stopped. I went to La Castris and took her poor little hands, so thin and cold, and kissed them many times, as her lovers used to do in former days.

"Three days later I left Paris for the provinces.

When I returned, after two years, that corner of hedges and quiet walks had been destroyed to make way for modern improvements. I wondered what the old couple did without their garden and its beloved memories. Were they wandering through the modern streets, like exiles without hope? Or were they dancing a fantastic minuet among the cypresses of some churchyard?

"The remembrance haunts me. It stays with me like a wound. You will find that very ridiculous, no doubt!"

The False Gems

GUY DE MAUPASSANT

Monsieur Lantin had met the young woman at a soirée and at first sight had fallen madly in love with her. She and her mother were simple honest people and the girl was the type of virtuous woman whom every sensible young man dreams of winning for life. Monsieur Lantin had a snug little income and he thought that he might safely assume the responsibilities of matrimony. So he proposed to this model young girl and was accepted.

He was unspeakably happy with her. She managed his household so cleverly and economically that they seemed almost to live in luxury. She lavished the most delicate attentions on her husband and the charm of her presence was so great that six years after their marriage Monsieur Lantin loved her even more passionately than during the first days of their honeymoon.

He felt inclined to blame her for only two things—her love of the theatre and a taste for false jewelry. Her friends frequently got her a box at the theatre and then her husband was obliged to accompany her, although the plays always bored and tired him after a hard day at the office. After a time he begged her to get some lady of her acquaintance to go with her—and after much persuasion she consented.

Now, with her love of the theatre, came also the desire to adorn herself. Her dresses remained simple and in good taste, but she began to wear huge rhinestones that glittered and sparkled like real diamonds. She had strings of false pearls and bracelets of imitation gold.

Her husband often remonstrated with her, saying, "My dear, as you cannot afford real diamonds you ought to appear adorned with your beauty and modesty alone."

But she would smile and say, "What can I do? I am so fond of jewelry. It is my only weakness. Ah, cheri, we cannot change our natures." And she would roll a pearl necklace around her fingers and say, "Look, aren't they lovely? See how they glow. One would swear they were real."

Monsieur Lantin would smile and say, "You have Bohemian tastes, my dear."

Sometimes in the evening she would bring out the box of trash, as Monsieur Lantin called it, and examine the false gems with a passionate and strange attention. Often she would put a necklace around her husband's neck and say, "How funny you look! Oh, cheri, how funny you look with the gems around your neck!" Then she would throw herself into his arms and kiss him affectionately.

One winter evening she went to the opera and came home chilled through and through. A week later she was dead. Monsieur Lantin's grief was so great that his hair grew white in a month. He could think of nothing but the smile, the voice, the charm of his dead wife.

Time, the healer, did not assuage his sorrow. Everything reminded him of the lost joy of his existence. His affairs began to go from bad to worse. His income no longer covered his own immediate needs and he wondered how his wife was able to buy such rare wines and such excellent delicacies. He incurred some debts and was soon reduced to poverty. And then he thought of the false gems. Up to the last his wife had continued to make purchases, bringing home new jewels almost every evening.

He decided to sell the heavy necklace that she seemed to prefer. Although it was only paste he thought it ought to bring six or seven francs. He took it to a jeweler's shop and went in, a little ashamed to expose his poverty and to offer such a worthless article for sale.

"Monsieur," he said, "I would like to know what this is worth."

The merchant took it and examined it. Then he called a clerk and they conferred in undertones, going over the necklace stone by stone.

Monsieur Lantin was annoyed at all this fuss and was on the point of saying, "Oh, I know well enough it's not worth anything," when the jeweler said, "Monsieur, this necklace is worth from twelve to fifteen thousand francs, but I cannot buy it unless you tell me how you got it."

Monsieur Lantin opened his eyes. "But—are you sure?" he stammered.

"You can go elsewhere and see whether anyone will offer you more. I consider it worth fifteen thousand at the very most. Come back here if you can't do any better."

Monsieur Lantin took the necklace and left the store.

Once outside he felt inclined to laugh. "Stupid fool! I ought to have taken him at his word. He can't tell paste gems from real."

He went into a store on the Rue de la Paix. As soon as the proprietor saw it he said, "Oh, yes, I know it well. It was bought here."

"How—how much is it worth?" said Monsieur Lantin.

"Well, I sold it for twenty thousand francs. I'm willing to take it back for eighteen thousand, when you tell me how it came into your possession."

"Until this moment," said Monsieur Lantin, "I thought it was paste."

The two men stared at each other. Then the jeweler said, "Will you tell me your name, monsieur?"

"My name? My name is Lantin. I live at number 16 Rue des Martyrs."

The merchant looked through his books and said, "Yes, monsieur, that is right. The necklace was sent to Madame Lantin, 16 Rue des Martyrs, July 20th, 1876." Monsieur Lantin neither moved nor spoke and after a moment the jeweler said, "Will you leave the necklace here for a day? I will give you a receipt. I would like to—make a few inquiries."

"Certainly," answered Monsieur Lantin, in a daze. "Certainly. Yes, I'll leave it here."

He went out and wandered aimlessly along the streets, trying not to face what was in his mind, trying not to think. Suddenly he stopped, flung up his arms and fell to the ground unconscious. When he was able to get home he locked himself in his room and no one saw him until the next day.

In the morning he went out, but he did not go to his office. He went back to the jeweler's in the Rue de la Paix. Twenty times he tried to force himself to go in, but could not. At last he summoned his courage, turned the knob and entered the store.

The proprietor came forward at once and offered him a chair. The clerks looked at one another knowingly.

"Ah, well, Monsieur Lantin," said the jeweler, "I have made inquiries and if you still wish to dispose of the gems I am ready to pay you the price I offered."

"Yes," said Monsieur Lantin. "Yes. I wish to—get rid of them." He took the money, signed a receipt and turned to go. At the door he looked back. "I have other gems—from the same source. Will you buy those, too?"

"Certainly, monsieur. I shall be most happy to buy whatever you wish to dispose of."

"I will bring them," said Monsieur Lantin.

The large earrings were worth twenty thousand francs, the bracelets thirty-five thousand, a set of real emeralds and sapphires fourteen thousand, a gold chain with a pendant forty thousand. Altogether the "false gems" came to about two hundred thousand francs.

The jeweler remarked, "Well, monsieur, there was a person who put all her money into precious stones."

"Yes," said Monsieur Lantin heavily. "After all, it is only another way of investing one's—earnings!"

That day he lunched at Voisin's and drank wine worth twenty francs a bottle. Then he hired a carriage and made a tour of the Bois. He dined at the Café Anglais and then went to the theatre.

Six months later he married again. His second wife was a very virtuous woman with a violent temper. She caused him much sorrow.

The Last Lesson

ALPHONSE DAUDET

1840–1897

I was late starting for school that morning and I was in great dread of a scolding, especially as Monsieur Hamel had said that he would question us about participles and I didn't know the first word about them. For a moment I thought of running away and spending the day out-of-doors. It was so warm and bright. But I hurried on, past the Town Hall where there were some Prussian soldiers standing and a big crowd looking at the bulletin board.

The blacksmith called after me, "Don't go so fast, bub. You'll get to your school in plenty of time."

I thought he was making fun of me and I ran through Monsieur Hamel's little garden and into the school room, all out of breath. I expected Monsieur Hamel to scold me, but he said very kindly, "Go to your place, little Franz. We were beginning without you."

The room was very still. I saw that our teacher had on his beautiful green coat, his frilled shirt and his little black cap, which he never wore except on inspection and prize days. On the back benches some of the village people were sitting—the mayor, the postmaster and several others. Everyone looked very sad.

Monsieur Hamel stood up and spoke gravely. "My

children, this is the last lesson I shall give you. The order has come from Berlin to teach only German in the schools of Alsace and Lorraine. The new master comes tomorrow. This is your last French lesson. I want you to be very attentive."

My last French lesson! Why, I hardly knew how to write. I should never learn any more. Oh, how sorry I was that I had gone off hunting birds' nests or sliding on the Saar! And Monsieur Hamel, too,—the idea that he was going away and that I should never see him again made me forget all about his scoldings.

Poor man, it was in honor of this last lesson that he had put on his fine Sunday clothes. And now I understood why the old men of the village were sitting there in the back of the room. It was their way of thanking our master for his forty years of faithful service and of showing their respect for a country that was theirs no longer.

I heard my name called to recite. What wouldn't I have given to be able to say that dreadful rule for the participle all through, very loud and clear, without one mistake. But I got all mixed up and stumbled and stood holding onto my desk, not daring to raise my eyes.

Monsieur Hamel said, "I won't scold you, little Franz. You must feel badly enough as it is. Every day we have said to ourselves, 'Bah! I've plenty of time! I'll learn tomorrow.' And now you see where we've come out. Now those fellows out there will have the right to say to you, 'How is it, you pretend to be Frenchmen and yet you can neither speak nor write your own language?' Your parents were not anxious enough to have you learn. And I—I have been to blame, also. Have I not often sent you to water my flowers, instead of learning your lessons?"

Then Monsieur Hamel went on to talk about the French language, saying that it was the most beautiful language in the world and the clearest and the most logical, that we must guard it and never forget it, because when a people are enslaved, if they hold fast to their language it is as though they had the key to their prison. Then he read the lesson to us and it seemed easy, so easy. It was almost as though the poor man wanted to give us all he knew before going away.

Then we had the lesson in writing and everyone worked so hard. The only sound was the scratching of pens. Once some pigeons cooed on the window sill, but no one paid any attention to them, not even the littlest ones. I thought to myself, "Will they make them sing in German, too, even the birds?"

Whenever I looked up I saw Monsieur Hamel sitting motionless in his chair and gazing first at one thing and then at another, as if he wanted to fix in his mind just how everything looked in that little class room. Why, just think of it, for forty years he had been there, in the same place, with his garden outside the window and his class in front of him. Nothing was changed. Only the benches were worn a little smoother and the walnut trees outside the window had grown a little taller. How it must have broken his heart to leave it all, poor man! To hear his sister in the room upstairs packing the trunks!

But he had the courage to hear every lesson, down to

the last. At the back of the room one of the old men had put on his spectacles and was holding his primer in both hands, reading aloud with the rest. You could see that he, too, was crying. Our last lesson!

All at once the church clock struck twelve and at the same moment the trumpets of the Prussians, returning from drill, sounded under our windows. Monsieur Hamel stood up, very pale.

"My children," he said, "I—I—" But something choked him. He could not go on.

He turned to the blackboard, took a piece of chalk and bearing on it with all his might he wrote as large as he could,

"VIVE LA FRANCE!"

Then he leaned his head against the wall and made a gesture with his hand.

"School is dismissed. You may go."

The Little Angel

LEONIDE ANDREYEV

1871–1919

At times Sashka wished that he could give up what is called living. He wanted to stop washing every morning in cold water, on which thin sheets of ice floated, to stop going to grammar school and being scolded, to feel no longer the pain in his back when his mother made him kneel in the corner all evening. He was only thirteen years of age, but it seemed to him that life would never end.

One Christmas Eve he came home late. He had been playing with the boys watching the fine dry flakes of snow floating in the air.

"It's about time you got back," said his mother crossly.

Sashka kept out of her way and went to join his father on the bench back of the stove.

"Sashka," whispered the old man, "the Svetchnikovs have invited you to their Christmas tree."

The boy stared at him incredulously. The Svetchnikovs were rich people. They lived in a big house that was warm and bright.

"You'd better go," said his father. "Perhaps they'll let you bring something home—something from the Christmas tree."

Later Sashka stood in the brilliant drawing room, with the other children. They walked on tiptoe around the big tree and the light from it fell on their eager faces. One of the little girls kept dancing up and down with delight, her hair, braided with dainty ribbons, bobbing against her shoulders. Sashka stayed shyly in a corner, staring at the tree. It blinded him, with its glitter of countless candles. It seemed hostile to him, even as the crowd of pretty well-dressed children who surrounded it. He wanted to creep away from them all and go some place where he could be alone.

Suddenly he leaned forward and his eyes opened. He had discovered on the tree something more beautiful than anything he had ever seen before. It was a little angel of wax, looking as though it were floating in the air. Its transparent dragon-fly wings trembled in the light. It seemed altogether alive, ready to fly away. The face held the impress of a feeling so lovely and so tender that Sashka felt as though he had known it all his life and loved it more than anything in the world.

The more he looked the more perfect the little angel became. He was so infinitely far off, so unlike anything the boy had ever known. Sashka felt that he would do anything to win the little angel. He avoided looking at it, lest he should direct the attention of the others to it. The children were trooping around the hostess, laughing and dancing. Sashka suddenly pushed them aside and went up to the tall lady.

"Will—will you do one thing for me? Give me the little angel!"

"What is the child talking about?"

"The angel! The angel there on the tree! Will you give it to me?"

"Oh, that's impossible. We're going to keep the tree decorated till the New Year."

Sashka felt as though he were falling over a precipice.

"I—I don't mean to be rude—or naughty. Only give me the little angel!"

"But it's impossible. Can't you understand that?"

Sashka caught hold of her dress and dropped on his knees. "Oh, give me the little angel! Please, please—the little angel!"

"Stand up! What a queer child you are! All right, I'll give it to you. But I don't know why you couldn't have waited till the New Year." She reached up and took down the little figure. "It's a beautiful thing. I don't know what you'll do with it. Wouldn't you rather have a picture book instead?" Sashka's agony became unbearable. He held out his hands silently. "Oh, well, take it! What a persistent boy!"

Sashka's hands as they seized his treasure were so soft and careful that the angel might have imagined himself to be flying in the air. He held it close to him and when the dainty wings touched his sunken breast he knew the first overwhelming joy that had ever come into his life.

He ran home and was glad to see that his mother was asleep, worn out with the day's work and vodka drinking. He went into the little room where his father lay, with a small cooking lamp burning on the table.

"Look!" he whispered and held the angel where his father could see it.

"Yes," said the old man. "He looks as though he were going to fly away."

"I see it, too," said Sashka in an ecstasy. "Look at his wings. Ah, but don't touch him!"

There fell upon the wall the shadows of the two heads, one big and shaggy, one small and round, bending towards the little angel.

"It's beautiful," said the father. "Why, Sashka, I believe you're crying. Come, you must go to bed. Your mother will hear us."

Sashka looked around for a place to lay the little angel. It could not stay on the floor, so he hung it to a nail that was fastened to the wall. Then he hurriedly threw into a corner the bundle of rags on which he slept.

"Why don't you undress?" said his father.

"What's the use? I shall soon be up again. I want to lie where I can see it the moment I wake up."

Sashka lay on his back in order to look at the little angel. He could see it in the smokey light from the lamp. Then he fell asleep and his father fell asleep, too. Peace lay on the weary face of the man who had lived his life and on the brave face of the little man who was just beginning it.

But the little angel, hanging by the hot lamp, began to melt. The lamp threw a melancholy light on the scene of gradual dissolution. The little angel seemed to stir. Over his rosy fingers rolled thick drops which fell upon the bench. To the smell of kerosene was added the scent of melting wax. The little angel gave a tremble, as though on the point of flight, and fell with a soft thud upon the hot flags. An inquisitive cockroach singed its wings as it ran around the formless lump of melted wax, climbed up the dragon-fly wings and twitching its feelers went on its way. Through the window the gray light of coming day crept in. The water-carrier, benumbed with cold, was already making a noise in the courtyard with his iron scoop.

Where Love Is God Is

LEO TOLSTOI

1828–1910

In a certain town there lived a cobbler, Martin
Avdeich by name. He had a tiny room in a basement,
with one window looking out on the street, through
which he could see the feet of the people who passed by
and recognize them by their boots. He worked well, he
did not charge too much, and if he could do a job by the
day required he undertook it. If not he made no false
promises. Martin had always been a good man, but in
his old age he began to think more about his soul and to
draw nearer to God. His wife died, and his children, one
by one. He was all alone now. One day he bought himself a testament in large type and began to read the
Gospels. After that he read every night and the more
he read the more clearly he understood what God required of him and how he might live for God.

One night he sat up late, reading in St. Luke's gospel.
"As ye would that men should do unto you, do ye also
to them likewise." And further on, "I entered into thine
house, thou gavest me no water for my feet, but she hath
washed my feet with tears and wiped them with the
hairs of her head. My head with oil thou didst not
anoint, but she hath anointed my head with ointment."
He read these verses and he thought, "He must have
been like me, that Pharisee. He, too, thought only of

himself—how to get a cup of tea, how to keep warm and comfortable. He took care of himself, but for his guest he cared nothing at all. Yet who was his guest? The Lord himself. If He came to me should I behave like that?"

And suddenly he heard a voice say, "Martin!"

He looked around, but no one was there. Then he heard quite distinctly, "Martin—Martin—look out into the street tomorrow, for I shall come."

Martin roused himself from his chair and looked all about. Then he put out his lamp and lay down to sleep.

The next morning he arose before daybreak and after saying his prayers he lit the fire and prepared his cabbage soup and porridge. Then he sat down by the window to work. But he looked out into the street more than he worked. He saw the old man, Stepanich, whose duty it was to help the house porter next door. He knew him by his boots, which were shabby old felt ones, galoshed with leather.

"I must be growing crazy with age. Stepanich comes to clear away the snow and I must needs imagine that the Lord Christ comes to visit me."

After he had worked a little more he saw that Stepanich had leaned his shovel against the wall and was resting himself. He was old and broken and no longer had the strength to move the snow. Martin put his awl on the table and tapped on the window. Then he got up and opened the door.

"Come in, Stepanich, warm yourself a bit. I'll give you some tea. The samovar is just on the boil."

"May God bless you," said Stepanich. He came in

and, lest he should leave marks on the floor, he began wiping his feet.

"Don't trouble," said Martin, "I'll wipe up the floor. It's all in the day's work. Come, friend, sit down and have some tea."

The old man took a tumbler full, poured it into his saucer and began to blow on it. "Are you expecting someone?" he asked.

"Well, no," said Martin. He looked out into the street for a moment and then he said slowly, "No, I'm not expecting anyone. Come, drink some more. Have another glass."

After a while the old man got up to go. "Thank you, Martin Avdeich," he said.

"You're very welcome. Come another time. I'm glad to have a guest."

Stepanich went away and Martin sat down and worked some more. After a time he saw a young woman, poorly dressed, with a baby in her arms. She was trying to shelter the child from the wind, though she had on only thin rags of clothes and had hardly anything to wrap around the baby. Martin went to the door.

"My dear, don't stand out there with the baby in the cold. Come inside. You can wrap him up better in a warm place. Come this way. There, my dear, sit down and warm yourself and feed the baby."

"I haven't any milk. I've eaten nothing myself since yesterday morning."

Martin shook his head. He got a dish and some bread and poured the cabbage soup over it. Then he spread a cloth on the table.

"Sit down and eat and I'll mind the baby. Why, bless me, I've had children of my own. I know how to manage them."

The woman crossed herself and began to eat, while Martin played with the baby. But he didn't let it get his finger in its mouth, because his hands were all black with cobbler's wax.

"Haven't you any warmer clothing?" he asked the woman.

"How could I get warm clothing? I pawned my last shawl two days ago!"

Martin took the child over to its mother. Then he went to the wall where his things were hanging and brought back a cloak. "Here, take this. It will do to wrap around the baby."

The woman looked at him and burst into tears. "The Lord bless you, friend! Surely Christ Himself must have sent you to your window, or the child would have frozen."

"Yes," said Martin. "Yes, it was He who made me do it. It was no mere chance that made me look out. Here, take this money and get your shawl out of pawn."

The woman crossed herself and Martin did the same. Then he saw her out.

After she had gone he ate some cabbage soup, cleared away the things and sat down to work. But he did not forget the window. Every time a shadow fell across it he looked up. After a while he saw an old apple woman stop outside. A ragged little urchin ran up, seized an apple from her basket and tried to slip away. The old woman caught him and berated him, scolding and threatening to take him to the police. Martin went out and took her hand.

"Oh, come now, Granny, forgive him. Boys will do these things, you know. Now, young fellow, don't you run off! Come back here and ask Granny's forgiveness and don't do it again! There now, there's an apple for you. I'll pay you for it, Granny."

"He ought to be whipped!" said the old woman.

"Now, Granny, that's our way, but it's not God's way! If he should be whipped for stealing an apple what would be done to us for our sins? If the youngsters are thoughtless we must teach them better ways."

Martin went back to his work and after an hour or so it began to get dark. "Seems it's time to light up." He took down the Gospels and was about to open them when he heard a voice say,

"Martin, Martin, don't you know me?"

"Who is it?" said Martin.

"It is I!" said the voice. And out of a dark corner came Stepanich and smiled and vanished like a cloud. "It is I," said the voice again. And out of the darkness came the woman with the baby in her arms. She smiled and the baby laughed and they, too, vanished. "It is I." And there came the old woman and the ragged little boy.

And Martin's soul grew glad. He crossed himself and put on his spectacles and began reading the Gospel. "I was an-hungered and ye gave me meat. I was thirsty and ye gave me drink. I was a stranger and ye took me in.

Inasmuch as ye have done it unto one of the least of these my brethren ye have done it unto me."

And Martin understood that his dream had come true and that the Saviour had really come to him that day, and that he had welcomed Him.